Cabbage Tree

Kahikatea.

Kanuka

Kowhai

Rewarewa.

Totara.

OUR TREES

A NEW ZEALAND GUIDE

Frank Newhook

paintings by Elaine Power

d|b

David Bateman

While preparing this book I visited many bush areas, parks and private gardens in search of the specimens illustrated, and I would like to acknowledge the help I received from my friends Muriel, Bill and Malcolm Fisher, Ann and Jim Holdaway, and the Rangers of the Auckland Regional Authority Parks and the Tongariro National Park.

The reference books I consulted were: *100 Trees of New Zealand,* Audrey Eagle (Collins); *Trees and Shrubs of New Zealand,* A.L. Poole & N.M. Adams (Government Printer); *The Native Trees of New Zealand,* J.T. Salmon (A.H. & A.W. Reed).

ELAINE POWER,
Auckland

© 1982 Frank Newhook (Text), Elaine Power
(Illustrations)
First published 1982 by David Bateman Ltd,
"Golden Heights", 30/34 View Rd,
Glenfield, Auckland 10, New Zealand.

ISBN 0-908610-09-2

Typeset in 10/11 Times by Monoset Trade Services Ltd, Auckland, and printed in Hong Kong by Colorcraft Ltd. Design and production by Paper Dart, Auckland.

The endpapers present a selection of barks from New Zealand trees.

Jacket illustration shows:
1. Beech, **2.** kaihikatea, **3.** old rimu, **4.** totara, **5.** cabbage tree, **6.** rimu, **7.** titoki, **8.** kauri, **9.** rata, **10.** rimu, **11.** rewarewa, **12.** taraire.

Contents

Foreword

When I received the invitation to collaborate on this book on some native trees of New Zealand, I was conscious of the many first-class publications already on the market, written by respected colleagues and in many cases by personal friends. What could I add that was different? Well, the publishers' intention was to produce a book that would be appreciated for its artistic merit and, at the same time, reach a lay public that wished to recognise and learn more about some of the trees seen in daily life or on holiday travels. Having accepted the challenge posed by this invitation, I found myself delving more and more into a literature much of which was inadequately remembered or fascinatingly new to me. There were the incredible explorations, fraught with discomfort and danger, of such historical figures as Colenso, Bidwill and Dieffenbach. I renewed acquaintance with yet earlier accounts of epic travels, notably those of Cook, first accompanied by Banks and Solander, and then by the Forsters, father and son.

I soon came to realise why almost every author wishing to quote impressions of the impact the vegetation made on him, fell back on Sir Joseph Banks' much used quote, for Cook rarely lingered long enough to allow time for his botanists to visit the far more fascinating and impressive interior. Banks wrote in 1769-70 . . . '' . . .above this the banks of the River * were completely cloath'd with the finest Timber my Eyes ever beheld of a Tree** we had before seen but only at a distance in Poverty Bay and Hawkes Bay thick woods of it were every where upon the Banks, every tree as strait as a pine & of immense size . . .''

It is interesting that Alison Drummond, in *Married and Gone To New Zealand,* her account of a trip from Thames to Tauranga in 1846 by Bishop Selwyn, should quote Mary Ann Martin of Judge's Bay, Auckland, on the identical topic. '' . . . a canoe was lent to us for six weeks on very easy terms and we were soon paddling along the coast till we entered the wide mouth of the Waihou River, called by the English the Thames. To our right another river ran into the gulf, fringed at the mouth by an extensive wood of white pine trees . . . a sharp bend brought us into sight of loveliness, such as one can never forget. The river became deep and narrow, and wound for many miles through a forest . . .'' Now fertile farm land!

Perhaps what I value most was renewal of acquaintance with Leonard Cockayne's *Vegetation of New Zealand* published in 1928. I had learned as a student to respect him as an incredible observer and thinker and had dipped into his *Vegetation.* In my subsequent career as a plant pathologist the name Leonard Cockayne still cropped up on occasion. Now, given an opportunity to indulge my basic botanical bias towards our native flora and vegetation, I can look back on my most recent experience – the valuable and fascinating one of reading everything Cockayne had to say about each of the trees that Elaine Power and I offer you in this book. What we describe between us is not an exhaustive list of our major New Zealand tree species– a few such as pukatea and hinau must await similar treatment in a later volume.

* The R. Waihou near Thames
** Kahikatea

I have drawn widely on many sources for my accounts, choosing what I felt were the items of greatest interest. There is a pattern in my selection and presentation, though I have tried to keep the latter as informal as possible for the sake of the reader. I have included aspects of family and geographic relationships because our flora is best seen in the context of its neighbouring regions. Although New Zealand was once joined to Australia, as part of the massive southern continent of Gondwanaland, that was over seventy five million years ago. "Continental drift" effectively separated our two countries so long ago in fact, that large physiognomically important genera such as *Eucalyptus* and *Acacia* across the Tasman have evolved without any sister species developing in New Zealand. We do have some ancient affinities with Australian flora, but it is easier to trace relationships northwards to the Pacific and South-east Asia. Also, as evidenced by Antarctic fossils, we can trace relationships via old southern land connections with South America and Australia — the southern beech genus *Nothofagus* being the most obvious example.

New Zealand occupies a unique place in the study of plant geography, from the points of view both of its dramatic prehistory and unfortunately its also more recent dramatic impact of man. Some botanically valuable plant communities are lost forever, others are in jeopardy. I hope that this book, with others in the same "genus", will aid in the understanding and appreciation of our flora by lay people. This is necessary if we are to have more public and political acceptance of the need to preserve as much as possible of our fast-diminishing native plant cover.

FRANK NEWHOOK
Department of Botany, University of Auckland

Kauri
Agathis australis

*On the valley floor the Greeks would have built a temple to
Poseidon, upheld by his own great kauri boles for columns.*
                    Poenamo, John Logan Campbell, 1881

The kauri has dominated forests of northern New Zealand since
prehistoric times. In those far-off centuries when natural succes-
sion or lightning-started fires sounded the death-knell for kauri,
new generations of kauri forest became established to maintain the
species. In a mere century since European settlement, man has
almost eliminated those superb stands of one of the world's largest
trees. Only recently have we learned to preserve the remnants and
encourage regeneration of this magnificent species. Kauri is re-
nowned for its straight-grained, honey-coloured wood which is
now only released to the market in very small quantities for special
purposes such as boat-building. It is a member of the monkey
puzzle family, Araucariaceae, and has relatives of the same genus,
Agathis, in islands of the Western Pacific from the Philippines to
Fiji. Reflecting its tropical ancestry, its habitat is restricted to 38°S.

Apart from timber, kauri once supported another important
industry, the collection of kauri gum – solidified resin exuded from
bark wounds, used in high quality varnishes.

The kauri undergoes distinctive stages in its life cycle. Seedlings
go through a slender, leggy stage as they wait for openings to occur
in the canopy of a "nurse crop", perhaps tea-tree. As they emerge
into full light, they grow quite rapidly into the conical juvenile or
"ricker" stage. At about 70–100 years, upper branches begin to
form a permanent broadly-spreading crown, all lower branches
having been shed by an efficient self-pruning system. From then on
for many centuries, perhaps even up to twenty, straight-sided
trunks, topped by massive branches and leafy tufts, dominate the
forest, sometimes alone, sometimes in cathedral-like groves.

Flakes of bark are shed copiously from the straight-sided trunks
of older trees and accumulate around the bases with fallen leaves,
twigs and branches. They rot to form deep mounds of well-drained
humus that become permeated with masses of the tree's own
feeding rootlets.

*Juvenile leaves bronze or green, opposite or spiral; mature leaves
alternate or sub-opposite, 2 – 3 cm long, veins parallel. Male and
female cones on same tree (monoecious), in spring and early
summer; male 2 – 5 cm long, stout, cyclindrical, female 5 – 8 cm
diameter, globular, scales arranged spirally, disintegrating at time
of release of the winged wind-dispersed seed.*

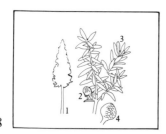

1. Ricker; 2. female cone; 3. male cone;
4. mature female cone

Titoki

Alectryon excelsus

A saying of old: He Peka tangata, apa he peka titoki: It is a human branch, it is not as if it were a titoki branch, that is to say a titoki branch dies, decays and is no more known, but the human branch lives on in its descendants.

Folklore of the Maori, Elsdon Best

Some fine titoki trees can be seen away from the forest, growing on farmland or as successful street trees, especially in the north. Titoki's attractive bright green leaves make it a popular urban tree; the lower branches remain leafy and in this context it does not grow embarrassingly tall although, in the forest, it sometimes reaches 17 m. Throughout its range, from North Cape to Banks Peninsula and Westland, it enjoys the alluvial soils of coastal and lowland forest but it is occasionally found in montane forests.

Alectryon is a genus with about twenty species distributed between Hawaii, Papua-New Guinea, the Pacific Islands, Australia and New Zealand. Its other relatives in the Sapindaceae or soap-berry family are mainly tropical.

Titoki is found only in New Zealand. It has a sister species, *A. grandis,* confined to Great King Island where, by 1945, it had been reduced by goats to a single surviving plant.

Leaves shiny, compound, 4 –6 pinnate, 10 –30 cm. Juvenile leaves are more deeply toothed that the adult. Flowers 3 – 4 mm, dark red stamens, sweet-smelling, but inconspicuous, crowded in panicles up to 30 cm. long. The showy fruit bursts out of a hard, woody capsule 8 – 12 mm long; a shiny black seed sits on a granulated fleshy cup or aril, coloured bright scarlet but variable in size from tree to tree. Flowers October – February. Fruits October – December (or later) of following year.

1. Ripe berries; **2.** mature tree

Wineberry
Makomako
Aristotelia serrata

Kirk (1899) cautiously suggested that, 'The berries seem likely to be used for colouring wine',
but the settlers' name, wineberry, may have arisen otherwise since the flowers vary in colour
from a faint rosy flush to deep claret.

Laing and Blackwell, 1907

This attractive small tree, growing to a height of 10 m belongs to the family *Elaeocarpaceae* which is predominantly Indo/Malaysian but has some American representatives. Other species of *Aristotelia* occur in Australia, Vanuatu and South America, but we have only two species in New Zealand.

Wineberry is found throughout the country, including Stewart Island, in some coastal areas, in lowland and montane forests, and even in subalpine situations. It is quick growing but not particularly long-lived. It is usually one of the first plants to appear after slips, on roadside clearings and in burned-off forest; almost invariably, its companion is the native tree fuchsia. Being light-demanding, it is also common on river banks and at the edges of the forest but rarely inside it. Like fuchsia, it is sometimes deciduous, especially in cold régions.

There seem to be two varieties of wineberry, one with light green leaves and bright red berries and the other with dark green leaves, purplish-below, and dark purplish-black berries.

Leaves opposite, ovate, 5 – 12 x 4 – 8 cm on long
petioles, doubly and irregularly deeply-serrate. Plants
are dioecious (male and female separate) the rose-
coloured flowers being small, 4 – 6 mm, but prolific in
panicles up to 10 cm long. Fruits red or black berries 4 –
5 mm diameter. Flowers September – December. Fruit
November – January.

1. Mature tree; **2.** mature fruit;
3. immature fruit and male flowers

Mangrove, Manawa
Avicennia resinifera

The quick and beautiful on the tree
Lights all the inner world.
It shimmers on the branches
Tells the wonder of a second life,

The Quick and the Beautiful,
Helen Shaw

When Banks and Solander collected their first mangrove specimens at Mercury Bay in 1769, they also collected pieces of amber-coloured resin lying amongst the roots. Bark, leaves and resin all seemed to have the same faint scent, so Solander assumed the resin, which was in fact kauri gum, had been exuded from the mangroves. So the species name "resinifera" meaning "yielding gum" is quite inaccurate, the gum having simply floated in on the tide!

The family Avicenniaceae is mainly tropical with several species found in India, Malaysia and Australia. *A. resinifera* is the only species in New Zealand and, like all its relations, it lives on mudflats, the edges of estuaries and tidal creeks.

Mangroves flourish in the far north, where they grow to about 10 m high but the further south they occur, the smaller they are, until at their 38° limit in Bay of Plenty they are barely half a metre high. On the west coast they extend scarcely as far as Kawhia. They must be one of the most unfairly maligned trees, largely because the swamps in which they grow are muddy underfoot and tend to become dumping grounds for urban rubbish! In fact, mangrove swamps with their rich animal life, form a vital link in aquatic "food chains". Mangrove roots grow outwards just below the mud surface with large numbers of peg-like breathing roots protruding a few centimetres above the mud. Seeds germinate while still on the plant, then fall off and float away, with a well-developed root ready to anchor the seedling between tides.

Leaves ovate or elliptic, to 5-10 cm long; glossy green above, white to buff below. Flower 4-6 in clusters at or near the end of shoots. Fruit a capsule up to 2 cm diameter. Flowers February – April. Fruits ripening in January the following year.

1. Immature trees; **2.** mature tree;
3. breathing roots; **4.** immature fruit

Taraire
Beilschmiedia tarairi

Tawa
B. tawa

New Zealand is the land of greenwood. The Forests are green, green everywhere and always, green of all hues, nothing but green, and...
New Zealand the Britain of the South,
Charles Hursthouse, 1957

Taraire and tawa belong to the largely tropical laurel family, Lauraceae, which also includes the bay tree, avocado, cinnamon and camphor. Both boast plum-sized fruit which are a favourite food of the native pigeon and were also an important item in early Maori diet. Tawa is especially prolific from 36° S, in podocarp-hardwood and beech forests to 42° S (N.W. Nelson, the Sounds, Seaward Kaikouras). It enjoys rich soil so, understandably, it has had to give way to farmland. Tawa once dominated three-fifths of the Waitakere Ranges and much of the Egmont-Wanganui and Thames districts. Where it grows with beech, the tawa tends to be on wetter valley sides with the beech on dry ridge tops.

In kauri forest, taraire may form a sub-canopy beneath kauri branches but when the kauri is absent, the taraire dominates. Sometimes it teams up with puriri to form groves containing a few totara, rimu, kohekohe and nikau, casting such a dense shade that very little grows beneath them. Taraire is important in coastal woodlands and it has a southern limit of 38° S.

Tawa is shade-loving, so its seedlings and saplings grow happily under sun-loving podocarps, waiting to succeed them when they die or are felled. This is one of the reasons tawa is so predominant in cut-over native bush.

Taraire: Tree to 24 m, relatively slender trunk, reddish-brown smooth bark. Leaves 13 cm x 8cm, leathery, dark green above, bluish beneath, edges down curved. Shoot tips with reddish hairy tomentum. Flowers bi-sexual, small, in panicles to 10 cm. Fruit a 3 cm oval purple-fleshed drupe with bluish bloom.
Tawa: Tree to 24 m smooth bark, almost black. Leaves lanceolate to 10 cm long, paired, bluish beneath. Flowers in panicles to 10 cm. Fruit a 2 – 3 cm oval drupe, ripening dark purple. Both flower in September – December. Both fruit in October/November – February or later.

1. Taraire; 2. mature taraire; 3. mature tawa; 4. tawa

16

Putaputaweta

Carpodetus serrata

Bush covered rise on rise,
Bulging the sky,
In its blue mystery,
Seasonlessly.

"South East, Tauranga", Pat Wilson,
N.Z. Poetry Yearbook 8

If the silver fern were not so firmly entrenched as our national emblem and we were looking for a native flower, I am sure putaputaweta would be a strong contender. It grows extensively in coastal and montane forest from the far North to Stewart Island. It is a versatile tree, reaching 10 m in height in the understorey of various lowland forests, including kahikatea swamp forest. Because of its light-demanding nature, it frequents stream sides, riverbeds and is important in advanced regeneration from scrub to forest. *Carpodetus* belongs to the family Escalloniaceae and the nine sisters to our solitary New Zealand species are found in Papua – New Guinea.

Putaputaweta has a distinct juvenile form with smallish leaves, often irregularly lobed, on slender zigzag interlacing branchlets. Branches of both juvenile and adult plants are in flattened tiers.

Leaves of adults thin but leathery, oblong to elliptic 4 – 6 x 2 – 3 cm, often with pale blotches between the veins; purplish below when young; finely serrate. Flowers white, small, 5 mm, but in crowded showy panicles. Fruits are globose capsules, 4 – 6 mm distinct median rim, green ripening to black. Flowers November – March. Fruit January – August.

1. Immature fruit; 2. mature tree;
3. underside of leaf (juvenile);
4. upper side of leaf (juvenile)

Cabbage Tree

Ti Kouka
Cordyline australis

They were, properly speaking, a new species of dragon-trees, with broad leaves (dracaena* australis) of which the central shoot when quite tender tastes something like an almond's kernel, with a little of the flavour of cabbage. We afterwards observed more of them in other parts of this bay.

A Voyage Round the World,
George Forster, 1878

Nothing less like a cabbage can be imagined! Nor does this tree conjure up a picture of a lily, yet is was once regarded as being in the family Liliaceae. Now it is recognised as a member of the Agave family with sister species in India, Malaysia, Polynesia, Queensland and South America. One of the five New Zealand species is found only on the Three Kings Islands and is aptly named *C. kaspar* after one of the Three Kings of biblical fame.

In 1880, William Colenso recorded how the early Maoris used their "cabbage" — drying the pith and roots of young trees in the sun before making a kind of porridge. Early European settlers found another use for the tree — they hollowed out the trunks and used them as fire-resistant chimneys for their shacks.

Cabbage tree trunks can reach quite large dimensions, as they can add to their diameter annually. Impressive specimens are frequently seen, in the sort of habitat they enjoy – swamps, sand dunes, coastal scrub and forest margins, river banks and dry hillsides – a versatile cabbage! If you ever have to dig one up you'll find it has a solid, starchy rhizome as thick as its trunk, plunging a metre or more down into the ground and sending out masses of brittle roots.

In early summer, the cabbage tree fills the air with a heavy, cloying scent from the hundreds of small white flowers that crowd onto the immense panicles up to 150 cm long. Insects, especially flies, are attracted in large numbers, ensuring successful pollination.

Cross-pollination between various species has led to numerous hybrids and the nursery trade now has several horticultural varieties.

Tree up to 18 – 20 m high. Leaves long-linear to 100 cm long, tufted, with older leaves drooping from the base. Large panicles with many hundreds of small white flowers. Fruits 4 mm diameter, whitish. Flowers October – December. Fruit January – April.

* Dracaena: an earlier name for Cordyline

1. Flowers and fruit; **2.** mature tree

Karaka

Corynocarpus laevigatus

Beautiful was Remuera's wooded shore, sloping gently to Waitemata's sunlit waters in the days of which I write . . . and the karaka with its brilliantly-polished green leaves and golden yellow fruit; contrasting with the darker, crimped and varnished leaf of puriri, with its bright cherry-like berry.

Poenamo, John Logan Campbell, 1881

Many distinguished botanists have used the word "handsome" to describe karaka. With its large, dark green, glossy leaves and substantial oval fruit turning golden when ripe, it is conspicuous as well as physically dominant. It is one of our most important coastal trees and occurs in the North and South Islands, extending to the Kermadec and Chatham Islands. However, in the South Island, where it is not so common, it has a southerly limit of Banks Peninsula and Westland. It has a few sister species in Vanuatu and New Caledonia.

It often forms natural groves for it tolerates deep shade and its seedlings grow where few other species can succeed. Clumps of karaka near pas, especially inland, usually mean they were deliberately planted by Maoris to ensure a ready supply of food. According to William Colenso, one of our famous early botanists, karaka kernels were once second only in importance to kumaras. The outer flesh was edible raw but the kernels had to be steamed for a considerable time, and then washed for two days in baskets laid in running water before being dried in the sun. It is now known that this treatment removed a highly poisonous glycoside that would otherwise have caused convulsions and death. Those who were affected by eating unprepared karaka kernels were buried up to their necks in sand to prevent crippling distortion should they survive. At worst, they died straight!

Tree to 20 m with smooth trunk. Large, alternate, elliptic, thick glossy dark green leaves 7−20 cm. Small pale greenish bi-sexual flowers in copious terminal panicles. Fruit a large 3−4 cm orange drupe. Flowers August − November. Fruit January − April.

1. Panicle of bisexual flowers;
2. mature tree;
3. mature fruit

Rimu
Dacrydium cupressinum

Kahikatea
Podocarpus (Dacrycarpus) dacrydioides

The Rimu (the most beautiful tree in the world when young) has branches very slender and pendulous, and the leaves very small, not much broader than hairs, and set all round the twigs, so that the tree looks as if it were composed of "Chenille" fringes.

Rambles in New Zealand,
J.C. Bidwell, 1839

These are not true pines, but part of a group of eighteen native conifers belonging to the podocarp family, including totara, miro, matai and tanekaha. The podocarps are amongst our most important trees, not only because they are our most valuable remaining source of indigenous timber, but also there are more podocarps of ancient lineage in New Zealand than in similar forests elsewhere. They dominated the ancient super-continent of Gondwanaland 75 million years ago before it drifted into separate masses, with our country on the outskirts. They have changed very little since those days. Pollen similar to that of the kahikatea is found in fossil pollen deposits 54 million years old. Rimu pollen goes back 37 million years.

Rimu is the most prolific of our podocarps and is found throughout the North and South Islands and even in subalpine situations on Stewart Island. It regularly grows to 35 m and, in lowland and montane forests up to 600 m, it occasionally reaches 60 m in height. Its yellowish-green heads with drooping branchlets, tower above everything else except other podocarps. The attractive pyramidal juvenile trees have an open and remarkably pendulous foliage.

Kahikatea is the tallest New Zealand tree, dwarfing even the rimu. Although widespread in mixed forest in the central North Island up to an altitude of 700 m, it especially enjoys swampy sites where its buttressed bases contribute to stability. Groves of kahikatea often grace wetter parts of farmland.

Rimu: Leaves are pointed scales 3 – 6 mm long. Male cones (strobili) up to 1 cm long shed pollen in spring; the female "cone" when ripe from midsummer to autumn has a 4 mm black seed on a juicy red receptacle enjoyed by birds.
Kahikatea: Leaves of juveniles are feathery and flattened compared with the 1 – 2mm pointed adult scale leaves. Male strobili are similar to those of rimu; also the seeds, which are borne on a fleshy receptacle ripening to orange or bright red in autumn. Heavy seed crops occur every 2 – 3 years.

1. Mature rimu; **2.** juvenile rimu;
3. juvenile kahikatea; **4.** mature
kahikatea; **5.** kahikatea branchtip and fruit

Kohekohe
Dysoxylum spectabile

... the sounding caratact
Haunted me like a passion; the tall rock
The mountain, and the deep and gloomy wood,
Their colours and their forms, were then to me
An appetite; a feeling and a love.

Wordsworth via Colenso

It's probably not widely known that kohekohe can claim relationship to the noble mahogany in the family Meliaceae. It has been listed as a native timber tree but the supply of available, worthwhile sawlogs is now almost non-existent. However, its red wood has made some fine furniture.

Kohekohe is an excellent example of cauliflory — not because it produces edible heads, but for its capacity to produce prolific, pendulous panicles of waxy white flowers up to 30 cm long on thick branches and trunks — in mid winter. It has a largely tropical ancestry and is usually found in coastal forest and scrub associations, sheltering behind a fringe of more salt-tolerant trees. However, it also grows inland in relatively frost-free situations and in rain-forests where it is joined by other semi-coastal species like karaka, kawakawa, titoki, ngaio and akeake. It loves fertile soils but areas where it used to grow have long since been converted to farmland. Its main habitat is from North Cape to Cook Strait and across to the Marlborough Sounds, with a southern limit of about 41° 30'.

Kohekohe and puriri often grow together, and the large compound leaves with prominent veins and wavy edged leaflets, about 13 x 4 cm, are confusingly similar. However, there is a major difference; puriri leaves are palmate with leaflets all arising from a common point, whereas the kohekohe leaves are pinnate, usually with 4 pairs of essentially opposite leaflets below one that is terminal.

Tree to 17 m; large, equally-pinnate leaves, base of petiole swollen. Flowers waxy white about 3 cm diameter in pendulous panicles up to 40 cm long. Seed capsules almost round, 2.5 cm, green when ripe, splitting to reveal bright red arils surrounding 2 seeds in each of 3 –4 cells. Flowers June –October (heavy in alternate years). Fruit February – September over 12 months later.

1. Mature fruit;
2. flower panicles on mature tree;
3. flowers

26

Puka, Akapuka

Griselinia lucida

Lo! in the middle of the wood,
The folded leaf is wooed from out the bud
With winds upon the branch, and there
Grows green and broad, and takes no care.

"The Lotus Eaters", Tennyson

This tree shares its shorter Maori name, puka, with the even larger leaved *Meryta sinclairii* also often cultivated in parks and gardens. However, *Griselinia* belongs to another family, Cornaceae, containing the largely Northern Hemisphere dogwoods. There is one other species in New Zealand, *Griselinia littoralis*, kapuka or papauma, plus six others in Chile.

Griselinia lucida grows abundantly in coastal and lowland forests of both North and South Islands. It may grow to a tree 8 m high but it is more likely to be found as an 'epiphyte' perching high in the branches of major forest trees, perhaps beginning life in a clump of long-leaved *Astelia*. From this lofty perch, it sends its distinctive, deeply-furrowed roots down to the ground. On Rangitoto Island, it is very happy to grow directly on slabby lava rocks, just like some other epiphytes.

Griselinia littoralis is similar, but is terrestrial and has smaller leaves. Its name *littoralis* means shore growing but this is somewhat misleading as it is often found growing at higher altitudes as well as in coastal forest.

Both species are popular with horticulturists, especially the variegated forms.

Chief characteristics for identification of G. lucida *are ovate-oblong, round-tipped, thick textured, unequal-sided (oblique) glossy leaves and furrowed root. Berries green, ripening to purplish black, 6-8 mm. Flowers October—January for both. Fruit December — August for both.*

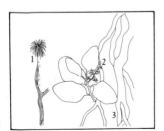

1. Mature plant showing climbing habit;
2. immature fruit; **3.** aerial roots

Rewarewa, N.Z. Honeysuckle
Knightia excelsa.

For once a kind of lotus-eater − enjoying
The wild odour of the forest flowers,
The music of the living grass and air,
The emerald light of leaf-entangled beams −
Which drowns the sense.

Wordsworth via Colenso.

Rewarewa could be thought of as a ''lonely'' species as it is one of only two members in New Zealand of the huge Protea family, represented by almost a thousand species in Australia and South Africa. On the ground, however, it is far from lonely, being an important member of several plant communities from North Cape to the Marlborough Sounds in coastal, lowland and montane forests and in advanced regeneration from scrub.

Rewarewa once played an important part in the ancient forests of the North Island — for example in the tawa forest of the Waitakere Ranges and the Thames region and in the totara forests of the King Country. Its columnar crowns, like so many lombardy poplars or kauri rickers emerge strikingly from other shrubs and trees but sometimes one has to look twice to distinguish rewarewa from young kauris as they both stretch for the light they enjoy.

New Zealand honeysuckle has been the common name for rewarewa since Charles Heaphy wrote about it in 1842, noting the similarity of its curled-back petals to the common honeysuckle. However, the sweet-smelling shrub *Alseuosmia* more appropriately shares the same common name.

Tree to 30 m with dark smooth bark. Leaves hard-textured, up to 20 cm long, coarsely dentate, linear-lanceolate; juveniles up to 30 cm, softer and acutely serrate. Flower buds tubular, red-brown, splitting into 4 perianth segments which curl back to the base and fall off to leave the red styles. Fruits boat-shaped, woody with persistent styles. Flowers October − December. Fruits 12 months later.

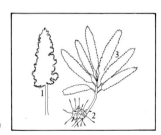

1. Mature tree; **2.** flowers;
3. dentate leaves

Tea Tree: Manuka   Kanuka
Leptospermum scoparium   L. ericoides

On the first day after our arrival we found a beautiful tree in flower, something related to the myrtle-genus, of which an infusion had been drank instead of tea on Capt. Cook's former voyage. We immediately repeated the experiment with great eagerness ... Its leaves were finely aromatic, astringent, and had a particular pleasant flavour at the first infusion; but this fine taste went off at the next filling up of the teapot, and a great degree of bitterness was then extracted. We therefore never suffered it to be twice infused. The use of this plant, which became general among our crew, probably contributed greatly to restore their strength, and to remove all scorbutic symptoms.

George Forster, 1878

If ever a plant could be regarded as a "universal aunt" in our flora it must be manuka, the "red" tea tree (red refers to the colour of its wood; kanuka is white). There is hardly a plant community in New Zealand, Three Kings or Chatham Islands, from sea level to subalpine and even alpine belts, that does not boast manuka. It is often a "nursemaid" for young seedlings of species that will later dominate it. It is our most successful native weed, along with bracken. Most of the time it grows with its slightly less versatile sister, kanuka, which refuses to be crowded out and eventually grows to 16 m.

Manuka has had a heyday since the arrival of man with his desire to cut and burn. Tremendous germination takes place when seed is freed from capsules opened by heat. Thickets with crowded straight stems can be found on sand, clay or rock, rolling hills, swamps and bogs or serpentine mineral belts, and it happily takes over pasture as the wind blows its powder-light seed.

The growth form of both tea trees varies greatly from upright trees or shrubs to dwarf scrub or prostrate mats, sprouting roots from creeping stems. Some of this is genetic but much of it is a reaction to sour soil and shearing winds on dune or alpine crest.

Flower colour varies, too, with a tendency towards pink in the far North. Horticulturists in New Zealand and California have developed many spectacular strains by breeding and selection. Natural hybrids between the two species sometimes make identification difficult. Tea tree is often spelt "ti-tree" but this name rightly belongs to the cabbage tree. *Leptospermum* belongs to the myrtle family Myrtaceae with ratas and pohutukawa, along with the prolific eucalypts on the other side of the Tasman. The majority of other members of the genus are in Australia, with a few in Malaysia and New Caledonia.

Manuka: Shrub or tree to 4 m, grey-brown bark shed in long strips. Leaves ovate-lanceolate 4 – 12 x 1 – 4 mm, sharp pointed. Flowers solitary, usually white, 6 – 12 mm. Capsules broad, 4 – 6 mm.
Kanuka: Shrub or tree to 16 m, bark as in manuka. Leaves are slimmer and less pointed than manuka, flowers are smaller, 3 – 6 mm and more crowded; capsules smaller, 2 – 4 mm, and narrower. Manuka flowers September – June. Kanuka flowers September – January.

1. Manuka flower and mature fruit;
2. manuka; **3.** kanuka flower and mature fruit; **4.** mature kanuka

N.Z. Cedars:
Kawaka, Kaikawaka and
Southern Kawaka, Pahautea

Libocedrus plumosa, L. bidwillii

Hail, old patrician trees, so great and good!
"Of Solitude", Abraham Cowley, 1618-1667

Literally, the Latin name *Libocedrus* means "fragrant cedars"; the first, *plumosa,* with feathery foliage and the second, *bidwillii,* named after an early botanical collector, J.C. Bidwill, who visited New Zealand in 1839. He wrote a fascinating account of his pioneering excursion into the centre of the North Island and his excitement at seeing Lake Taupo; also his was the first European ascent of Ngauruhoe. Appropriately, some of the most notable stands of southern kawaka are still to be found in that volcanic central region. Early classifications describe the genus as extending to California, Chile, China and Japan but it is now split and only our two species, with three others in New Caledonia, remain in *Libocedrus.*

Both species are noted for their pyramidal form and their distinctly horizontal branches. Their chestnut-coloured bark peels off in long strips. Although kawaka grows generally throughout New Zealand, it has a peculiar gap in its distribution from Hawkes Bay and Taranaki to Cook Strait. However, it appears again in N.W. Nelson, its southerly limit. It is normally a scattered inhabitor of lowland forest but it also contributes to an unusual stunted forest on higher parts of the Coromandel Range.

Southern kawaka has a northerly limit of 36° but otherwise grows in both islands in montane and subalpine situations except in Westland where it descends to about 250 m. It is commonly found in bog forests of the volcanic plateau, Egmont and South Island growing to 12 m, "shorn" to a mere 2–4 m in exposed situations.

Male "cones" (strobili) are produced copiously in the spring. Female cones are small, consisting of 4 woody scales, each with a spine; two of these bear winged seeds which are shed about a year after the spring in which the cone was pollinated.

34

1. Immature tree; 2. mature cedar; 3. male flowers; 4. female flowers

Pohutukawa, Christmas Tree
Metrosideros excelsa

... about forty feet from the rocks grew the celebrated Reinga pohutukawa. The root grew out a few feet, washed and bleached, which our guide gravely assured us was done by the feet of the spirits.

William Colenso, 1844

The common name "Christmas tree" unquestionably means pohutukawa, even though the main flush of its flowers is often over before Christmas Day! However, early or late, in a short or long season, in an "on" or "off" year, the pohutukawa blazons its presence on cliffs, in coastal shrub and forest from Three Kings Islands to Poverty Bay and North Taranaki (36° – 39°). It plays an important part on off-shore islands within its range.

On Rangitoto Island it is at home on bare scoria lava, just like its sister species *M. collina* on Mt. Kilauea, Hawaii. There, once established, its fallen leaves form humus on which other species can grow and enjoy the shade. Northern rata, another member of the genus, grows on the higher centre of Rangitoto Island along with pohutukawa, and numerous hybrids are also found.

On the Kermadec Islands, 800 km NE of New Zealand, there is another species, *M. kermadecensis,* closely related to our pohutukawa and to the Hawaiian *M. collina*. It has a slightly smaller rounder leaf than the pohutukawa and flowers throughout the year, a feature that has led to its wide use in horticulture. However, it lacks a midsummer blaze of colour, a feature which could in the long term be detrimental to our own pohutukawa as the two species readily hybridise.

Pohutukawa characteristically perches on coastal cliffs from which it projects with heavy horizontal branches and where it anchors itself with fantastic grappling root systems. The natural curves in the branches of coastal pohutukawa were once used for the bows and ribs of boats. It is interesting to note that the name *Metrosideros* translates as "heartwood of iron".

Pohutukawa has also formed extensive forests inland around Tarawera and other thermal region lakes.

The scarlet flower heads are conspicuous with their long red stamens, lightly tipped with golden pollen sacks. Petals are inconspicuous. Pollination is effected by birds and insects feeding on nectar in cups surrounding the stigmas in the centres of flowers.

Shrub or tree to 25 m high, often with several trunks; bark grey-brown, furrowed and stringy. Leaves elliptic-oblong up to 10 cm long, tough, shiny above and white below. Prone to browsing by possums. Seed very fine, windblown, borne in capsules 7 – 9 mm long. Flowers December – January. Seed shed February – April.

1. mature tree; **2.** flower buds and flowers

Ratas: Northern   Southern
Metrosideros robusta   M. umbellata

Clematis wound
In and above and round
Rata on high
Running across the eye
Like a vein's red dye

"South East, Tauranga", Pat Wilson,
N.Z. Poetry Yearbook 8

The "gigantic scarlet flowering myrtle" that impressed Sir Julius Vogel in 1875 is familiar to all lovers of our native bush. The tree usually begins life as an epiphyte perched high in the crown of a forest tree such as rimu. From that lofty perch, roots descend to the ground, giving off lateral roots which girdle and may eventually strangle the host. This root system fuses to form a massive trunk which may still show its root origins long after the original support tree has rotted away.

Northern rata grows on the Three Kings Islands, throughout the North Island and in Nelson Province, overlapping considerably with southern rata which is found from 36° in the north (about Dargaville) right through to Stewart Island and several subantarctic islands, including Auckland Island. The truly terrestrial southern rata, alone or with kamahi, dominates its own extensive forests, particularly in the South Island where it may suffer enormously from possum browsing. However, both ratas grow in mixed coastal, lowland and montane communities. Their wide-spreading branches, with billowy layers of foliage, give the impression of many long-handled open umbrellas. Both species have papery bark, peeling off in strips.

Ratas belong to the New Zealand myrtle family, and their genus, *Metrosideros* has ten species in New Zealand (excluding the Kermadecs) all of which, except for pohutukawa, northern and southern ratas and *M. parkinsonii,* are climbers with red, orange or white flowers. Pollination is by nectar-eating birds and insects.

Trees up to 15 m (southern) or 25 m (northern). Leaves of the southern rata taper elegantly to a point and are dotted with tiny oil glands but those of the northern rata are blunter, with a small notch at the tip. Flowers have very small red petals but conspicuous red stamens 2 – 3 cm long. Seeds very fine in 3-valved capsules. Northern rata flowers November – January. Southern rata flowers November – March. Seeds shed 1 – 2 months later.

1. Flower; **2.** mature tree

Beeches: *Mountain*   *Silver*
Nothofagus solandri var. cliffortioides   *N. menziesii*

Red
N. fusca

There at the foot of yonder nodding beech,
That wreathes its old fantastic roots so high,
His listless length at noontide would he stretch,
And pore upon the brook that babbles by.

"Elegy Written in a Country Churchyard", Gray, 1716-1771

We have five beeches in New Zealand – mountain, silver, red, hard and black (the last two are not illustrated). They are all forest dominants and have two particularly important features. Firstly, as with almost all southern hemisphere beeches, they are evergreen, whereas the northern hemisphere members of the same family, Fagaceae, which includes oaks and chestnuts, are deciduous.

Secondly, New Zealand beeches show striking irregularities in their distribution. They are not found on Egmont, nor in a 200 km area in Central Westland nor on Stewart Island. It is believed that the Westland gap was caused by the virtual elimination of plant life from that region during the great Ice Ages about ten thousand years ago. The first trees to grow again after the final thaw would have been the podocarps, whose seeds are distributed by birds, and the rata and kamahi, which have wind-blown seeds. The beech could have encroached only slowly, for beech nuts, when eaten by birds, are fragmented and the seed digested, thus preventing long-range distribution. Volcanic activity and extreme cold could have triggered comparable situations on Egmont and Stewart Island.

Various beech species are found in Papua-New Guinea, Australia, New Caledonia and temperate South America. Our New Zealand species are found only in the North and South Islands. Their distribution is interesting. Hard beech occurs from near Kaitaia 35° S, to about

Continued on page 42

1. Silver beech; 2. red beech; 3. mountain beech; 4. mature mountain beech tree

Greymouth 42° S; silver beech commences in the Coromandel Range near Thames; red beech comes in slightly further south at Te Aroha, and mountain beech starts about 38° S. All, except for hard beech, are found virtually as far south as Foveaux Strait. However, one intriguing point is that silver beech is the only beech found in the Catlins State Forest Park east of Invercargill – probably because it doesn't have to compete with the aggressive mountain beech which, for some unknown reason, is completely absent from the S.E. region. As can be judged from its name, the mountain beech grows at much higher altitudes than its sister species.

The early Maori recognised both the close relationship and the major differences between species of beech. He called silver beech tawhai, grouped the rather similar red and hard beeches as tawhairaunui and, likewise, black and mountain beeches are tawhairauriki.

Trees to 25-30m, foliage in characteristically horizontal layers. Flowers on all beeches are monoecious – unisexual flowers on the same plant; male flowers are virtually a cluster of red stamens; female "cupules" 5 – 10 mm, ripening to a hard nut. Every now and then there is a prolific flowering or "mast" year. Red, hard and black beech flower September–December. Silver and mountain beech November – January.

Tanekaha, Celery Pine
Phyllocladus trichomanoides

. . . I know, like the pioneers, the smell of this kind of wood smoke and that. I know that lancewood will burn the soot from the bricks, and tanekaha put it back again.

Hills of Home, E.M. Blaiklock, 1966.

This is an unusual tree, for what appear to be leaves are really flattened, green, leaf-like stems known as cladodes or phylloclades. Their true leaves are produced only on young seedlings and are up to 2 cm long, narrow and deciduous; on adult trees they are just tiny projections on the cladodes.

Tanekaha has a conical juvenile growth form similar to that of young kauri – its companion in the North. But it is not long-lived compared to the kauri, reaching a mere 300 to 500 years of age! Its main habitats are coastal and lowland forest scrub but there is a curious gap in its distribution. It flourishes from North Cape to about 40° S, is then absent south of a line from Taranaki to Hawkes Bay, but occurs again in Marlborough and N.W. Nelson.

Tree to 23 m, self-pruned trunk not unlike that of the young kauri with smooth bark and patches of grey lichen. The male cones (strobili) are in clusters of 5 –20 at the tips of the twigs. They are 10 –15 mm long and narrow. Female cones replace 4 –8 of the cladodes on fertile twigs separate from the male. Cones are small, made up of a few swollen bracts, each carrying a protruding seed about 3 mm long. Pollen and ovules mature late spring – early summer. Seeds are ripe 4 – 6 months later.

1. Juvenile tree; **2.** male cones

Totara
Podocarpus totara

Hall's Totara
P. hallii

Miro
P. ferrugineus

Matai, Black Pine
P. spicatus

Te totara wahi rua he aitua, kia kotahi he waimarie. A totara split in falling represents a misfortune, one that remains whole betokens good luck.

Folklore of the Maori, Elsdon Best

Totara has earned its fame as one of New Zealand's most versatile timbers. Its straight-grained durable wood made it ideal for Maori canoes and for the structural or ornamental timbers of meeting houses; its thick, stringy bark was used for thatching. Totara's resistance to borer and rotting was soon recognised by European settlers who relied on it for a range of purposes such as fence posts, doorsteps, window frames and telegraph poles.

Totara is found in various types of forest, from exposed coastal areas to kauri and taraire forests. However, it is most common in the podocarp-mixed hardwood forests of the North Island and Westland where it may soar to a height of 30 m or more. Long before European times, totara forest was extensive in the now treeless parts of Canterbury and Central Otago, and the almost extinct forests of Banks Peninsula were apparently dominated by totara, Hall's totara and matai. In many places, totara is a vigorous colonist on farmland.

Hall's totara is distinguishable from its sister species by its thin, flakey, non-furrowed bark, its longer juvenile leaves and its shorter stature. It often overlaps totara in distribution and extends to higher altitudes, joining southern kawaka and kamahi on Egmont and in Westland. Incidentally, Hall's is the only totara on Stewart Island.

Matai is now relatively rare, and is found in many of the same areas as miro, rimu and totara. Both matai and miro have fine timber; miro is often sold as rimu but matai is harder and darker and, at one time, was prized for exposed flooring.

All podocarps have fleshy fruits which are attractive to birds which spread their seeds. In the totaras these are ovoid nuts a few mm long, borne on the tips of swollen fleshy stalks that ripen to bright red. Miro has substantial, 2 cm fleshy oval drupes that ripen purplish red with a glaucous bloom. Matai drupes are small, about 1 cm, almost round, and ripen to black.

Leaves of totara and Hall's totara are spirally arranged, sharp pointed, up to 2.5 cm long and 3 – 4 mm wide, longer on juvenile plants. Matai and miro leaves are in two rows, giving a flattened appearance to twigs – bluish below in matai. Pollen cones (strobili) are small and narrow in all species, and are on separate trees from female ovules. Fruits ripen November – February and may even be seen in May in the case of matai and miro.

1. Mature miro drupe; **2.** mature totara; **3.** totara; **4.** mature miro

Kowhai
Sophora microphylla
S. tetraptera

When the candles burn again in the Kowhai tree,
I shall return, remembering other springs
When the sky was a blue pool where dreamily
Clouds floated like silver swans with folded wings.

A.R.D. Fairburn

Some say that yellow kowhai should be our national flower– but which species? That's the question! *S. microphylla* is widespread throughout New Zealand but the less common *S. tetraptera* is often more spectacular and more popular as a garden tree. Along with pohutukawa, kowhais must be amongst our most beautiful trees. Pohutukawa celebrates Christmas, kowhai greets Labour Day. The kowhais are amongst our few deciduous native plants though they have hardly shed one season's leaves before the flower buds burgeon into cascades of undiluted gold followed shortly by new leaves.

An identical form of *Sophora microphylla* is found in Chile. Godley* records viable seed arriving in ocean currents on the Kermadec Islands, so the Southern American occurrence may be by luck rather than by ancestral distribution. He also discovered that seed could survive for three years in salt water.

S. microphylla grows happily on the coastline, lakeside, riverside and on edges of the forest. It flourishes on central North Island sandstones. *S. tetraptera* has similar habitats but only grows from East Cape, about 38° S, to the Ruahine Ranges, about 40° S.

Kowhai belongs to the pea family, Papilionaceae, noted for its ability to fix atmospheric nitrogen (and make it available for life in general) through the special bacteria-containing nodules on their roots.

Sophora microphylla: *tree to 10 m, pinnate leaves up to 15 cm long with 20 – 40 pairs of almost round to oval-oblong leaflets 5 – 10 mm long; clustered yellow flowers up to 4.5 cm long; pods up to 20 cm long, 4-winged.*
S. tetraptera: *trees to 12 m, similar to its sister species but leaflets longer, 15 – 35 mm and 10 – 12 pinnate. Both trees have graceful spreading crowns. Flowers October – November. Seeds shed autumn – winter following.*

* E.J. Godley, until lately Director, Botany Division, D.S.I.R. Lincoln.

1. Mature seed-pod; 2. *S. tetraptera* flowers; 3. mature tree *S. tetraptera*; 4. *S. tetraptera*

Puriri
Vitex lucens

The air was full of scent of the bush, the smell
of the ponga fronds, of the dead leaves of puriri
and the faint pungency of manuka.

Hills of Home, E.M. Blaiklock, 1966.

Growing as happily in urban streets of the north as in its native environment, the puriri, evergreen, and in flower and fruit for most of the year, tolerates drastic pruning whenever necessary.

Before European settlement, puriri forests occupied large areas of fertile volcanic soil in North Auckland, but the tree's value for fence posts, railway sleepers and houseblocks, as well as the agricultural desirability of the soil on which it grew, led to its downfall. However, we still see patches of it on the coast and inland, its rounded crowns bulging in the canopy of other trees.

Vitex is a large tropical and sub-tropical genus, extending from the North Cape to just over 39° S at the Mahia Peninsula and Cape Egmont. The family, Verbenaceae, is best known commercially for its much-sought after teak, and puriri's dark reddish-brown timber is equal in hardness to teak. It, too, is heavy and strong but its uneven grain makes the wood hard to work. Larvae of the huge, pale green puriri moth commonly drive large galleries through the trunks. Puriri's tropical affinities are reflected in its northerly and coastal distribution.

Tree to 20 m, trunk often massive and irregular, spreading, rounded crown; branchlets square in cross section; leaves palmate, 3 – 5 leaflets, each up to 12.5 x 5 cm (though basal 1 – 2 are smaller), wavy-edged, recurved midrib, veins keeled, glossy, deep green; dichotomously branched panicles, with up to 15 red, asymmetrical flowers 2 cm across; drupes 2 cm diam., bright red. Flowers almost all year round, especially June – October. Fruits likewise, especially February – September.

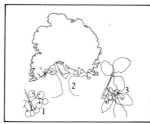

1. Mature ripe fruit; 2. mature tree;
3. flowers

49

Kamahi, Towai
Weinmannia racemosa

Tawhero, Towai
W. sylvicola

Fine hikers, these trees, no cliff has dared
Refuse foothold; but when walking in
From the river, man, stranger always, finds green...
That needs no steep height to refuse entrance.

"Rain Forest, Cascade Creek", Paul Henderson,
N.Z. Year Book, 1958-59

Kamahi is probably the most common major forest tree in our country, even though it grows no further north than the Thames region, about 37° S. In fact, it appears just as the kauri disappears! From there on, to Stewart Island, it plays an important role as an understorey or subdominant tree along with rimu, other podocarps, rata and beech. It grows at sea level in places, notably in northern Westland, but otherwise is usually found in lowland and montane forests and even in some subalpine situations. It displays its hardiness at high altitudes where it is often stunted and shorn by the wind. It is remarkably adaptable for a member of a mainly subtropical family, Cunoniaceae.

A notable example of kamahi forest is on Mt. Egmont where the massive irregular trunks and gnarled spreading branches are festooned with mosses, liverworts and filmy ferns; the whole community is aptly called a "goblin forest". Kamahi seedlings often begin life perched on a fallen log or half-way up a tree fern; roots which are sent down to the ground later contribute to the rugged appearance of the trunks of older trees.

Tawhero is about half the height of the kamahi, growing to a maximum of about 20 m. It has a distribution rather like kauri and only grows as far south as about 38° S.

Both kamahi and tawhero change their leaf form with age. Juvenile kamahi leaves are commonly trifoliate, and reduce to the simple condition as the plant matures. Tawhero juvenile leaves usually have up to 10 pairs of leaflets, reducing to 1 – 5 when the plant is adult. Both trees are readily identifiable by their paired, erect inflorescences up to 12 cm long, crowded with small white florets. Prolific flower and leaf buds give both a distinctly reddish appearance. Kamahi flowers December – January, seeds January – April. Tawhero flowers August – December, seeds November – February.

1. Tawhero seeds; **2.** mature kamahi; **3.** kamahi flowers

Raising Your Own Native Trees

This section of the book is intended as a guide for those who would like to propagate and grow a few native trees. Nothing quite matches the thrill and sense of achievement that comes from nurturing a plant from a seed or cutting through to a fine specimen in your garden.

General Principles

Trees are propagated either by seeds or by vegetative means such as cuttings, grafting or layering. Vegetative propagation produces a plant which is genetically identical to the parent and is the only way to reproduce named cultivars such as the many variegated and coloured-foliage forms of our native trees or, for example, the many fine coloured tea-trees. If you have a tree which has flowers of a better size, form or quantity than usual, a neater habit, or any other desirable characteristic that you wish to preserve, then it can be reliably reproduced only by vegetative propagation. This process of selecting good forms and propagating from them has until recently been sadly neglected by nurserymen producing native trees and shrubs.

Perfectly good plants can, of course, be raised from seed and sometimes may be the only way for species that are very difficult to strike from cuttings, but bear in mind that resulting plants will be much more variable.

Cuttings

Fortunately, you do not need sophisticated equipment to raise a few trees from cuttings. Many, particularly hardwoods, can be struck in the open ground in a shady corner, provided that you remember to keep them moist. A cold frame, preferably airtight and deep enough to accommodate the largest cuttings, will increase your chances of success. There are three main types of cuttings:

1. Softwood – soft growths usually taken after the first flush of growth in spring, or early summer. 8 to 15 cm long.
2. Semi-hardwood – shoots of the present season's growth which has not yet become fully woody. These are usually taken in summer and early autumn. 8 to 15 cm long.
3. Hardwood – made from fully ripened growth at the end of the growing season. Can be considerably longer, up to 30 cm.

The softer the cutting, the more protection it needs from drying out. Cuttings must not be allowed to wilt. If delay between taking the cuttings from the tree and preparing them for insertion in the frame is unavoidable, they should be stored in a slightly moistened polythene bag. Moderately vigorous, firm shoots should be selected for cuttings rather than over-vigorous soft, sappy or thin ones. They should be free of all pests or fungi.

Cuttings taken from plants growing in the wild are often harder to strike than those from plants already in cultivation as the latter have probably already been produced vegetatively several times.

When making cuttings, it is essential that a clean cut be made – the humble razor blade is an ideal tool. However, tougher hardwood cuttings may need a sharp knife or secateurs. Cuts should be made straight across just below a node or joint and the lower leaves trimmed off. When cuttings have large, soft leaves it is necessary to reduce transpiration by reducing the size of the top leaves also. Hormone rooting powders, if used, should be applied at this time. Insert the cutting into a sterilised rooting medium which may be entirely sand or, alternatively, a mixture of peat and sand. It should be inserted only deep enough to hold it upright and the medium then firmed lightly around the cutting. Water immediately and, if in a container, place in a closed propagating frame or outside in a shady corner.

Ensure the cuttings do not dry out, and remove any fallen, decaying leaves or cuttings which have died or started to rot at the base. Rooted cuttings may be potted up carefully in one of the potting mixes available from any garden centre.

Seed

Many native trees can be successfully raised from seed, but providing the normal requirements of warmth, moisture and air is not always sufficient. Some require special treatment prior to sowing to break their dormancy, as they may have a very hard seed coat which prevents the ready absorption of moisture. Kowhai seed, for example, if sown untreated will germinate very slowly and erratically and may take several years. If you rub the seeds between two sheets of glasspaper before sowing, most will germinate within a couple of weeks.

Other seeds require what is known as an 'after ripening period' and should be stratified. This means first removing any fleshy covering from the seed and then placing it between layers of damp sand or peat in a suitable container which should be placed during winter in the coolest part of the garden. In spring the seed is removed from the container and sown normally. Those living in the winterless north of New Zealand will have to use the refrigerator, but not the freezer compartment as the aim is to keep it as close to 1° C as possible in the presence of moisture.

Seed Sowing

For small quantities it is easiest to buy a proprietary seed-raising mixture, which should be moist but not wet, and firmed down to give an even surface on which to sow. Be especially careful with fine seed such as tea-tree or pohutukawa, as if sown too thickly it will produce spindly seedlings and the risk of disease is increased. Fine seed can be mixed with sand to bulk it up and make thin sowing easier.

Very fine seed should not be covered. Most other seed will germinate very well without covering with mix, but it is essential that it does not dry out at any stage and therefore it needs more regular attention if not covered. Larger seed can be covered with mix shaken through a sieve to a depth roughly equal to the diameter of the seed.

After sowing, partially immerse the container in water until the mix is thoroughly moistened. It will not hurt to leave it in the water overnight, then remove and allow the container to drain. Cover with a sheet of glass or fibrolite or place in a propagation frame. Inspect regularly for signs of germination and as soon as it starts, bring out into full light so that the seedlings do not become drawn. When the seedlings are large enough to handle they should be potted up or pricked out into trays if small. All containers, frames and tools used must be kept scrupulously clean.

How to propagate the trees mentioned in this book

Kauri – by seed which must be very fresh. The female seed-bearing cones ripen towards the end of February or the beginning of March. Leave the cone in a sunny dry place to open and shed its seeds. Sow as soon as possible. Try your luck with cuttings from young trees as well.

Rimu – by seed or semi-hardwood tip cuttings taken from young plants.

Kahikatea – usually seed.

Totara – easily raised from soft or semi-hardwood cuttings or from fresh seed. The golden form, *Podocarpus totara* 'Aurea' makes a very fine garden plant and is propagated by cuttings.

Miro – by cuttings or seed.

Matai – by cuttings of adult, not juvenile, foliage.

Tanekaha – seed or semi-hardwood cuttings which can be very slow.

Taraire and tawa – seed.

Nothofagus species (beeches) – seed if obtainable. Stratify.

Kamahi and towai – seed or cuttings.

Ratas – semi-hardwood cuttings.

Pohutukawa – cuttings or seed. The seed capsules should be collected when just starting to open and placed in a warm dry spot to shed the seeds. Young plants are often attacked by blister scale which causes puckering and distortion of young leaves. An occasional spray with Orthene insecticide gives excellent control. Whilst seed-grown plants can often take years, cuttings flower within 2 or 3 years of propagating. Yellow-flowered and variegated forms are best reproduced by cuttings.

Kohekohe – easiest from seed but will also strike from cuttings.

Puriri – seed, treated as for kowhai, or cuttings. As with any seed with a fleshy covering this should first be removed by placing the fruits in water and allowing to ferment for a few days, at which stage the flesh can easily be washed off and the seed sown.

Cabbage tree – easy from seed. Cuttings for named forms.

Titoki – seed, which takes 12 months to ripen on the tree.

Libocedrus – semi-hardwood cuttings which are slow, or seed.

Griselinia – cuttings, which are essential for the variegated forms of *Griselinia littoralis,* or seed.

Putaputaweta – seed or semi-hardwood cuttings.

Kowhai – seed scarified as described above, or cuttings of good forms. A dwarf cultivar *Sophora tetraptera* 'Gnome' comes true from seed.

Wineberry – cuttings or seed.

Rewarewa – seed.

Leptospermum – soft or semi-hardwood cuttings for the named cultivars. Or try some seed and see what you get!

Karaka – seed or semi-hardwood cuttings particularly for variegated forms.

TONY PALMER
Superintendent of Horticulture,
University of Auckland

Glossary and Map

aril:	an appendage to a seed, often fleshy
asteliad:	a member of the genus *Astelia*
bisexual:	flowers with both sexes functional
buttressed bases:	roots merging into trunk with flattened flange-like projections
cladode:	flattened stem functioning as a leaf
crown:	of a tree, the upper branch system, contributing to the canopy of a forest
cultivar:	a cultivated form or horticultural variety, usually vegetatively propagated
cupule:	a cup-shaped structure at the base of a flower or fruit
dentate:	with sharp teeth at right angles to the margin (of a leaf)
dominant:	of trees, out-topping others, contributing to the main canopy of a forest
drupe:	a fruit with the seed surrounded by a fleshy layer
genus:	a group of related species, the next higher level of classification being the family
glaucous:	of a distinctly bluish-green colour
globose:	rounded, almost spherical
globular:	see globose
glycoside:	a chemical combination between a sugar and another compound
Gondwanaland:	the ancient supercontinent from which the various Southern Hemisphere lands have separated and drifted apart in geological time
habitat:	the kind of place in which a plant grows
inflorescence:	a general term for a collection of flowering parts or for the arrangement of the flowers
lanceolate:	lance shaped; several times longer than wide, with widest part nearer to the base
littoral:	on or near the shore
monocotyledon:	a plant whose embryo has one cotyledon or seed leaf; veins usually parallel
monoecioius:	having unisexual flowers, with male and female on same plant
montane:	inhabiting mountainous country
ovate:	egg shaped in outline, attached by the broad end
ovule:	the structure which contains the egg or female sex cell and which develops into the seed
palmate:	radially lobed or divided, similar to digitate, spreading from centre like fingers of a hand
panicle:	an indeterminate inflorescence with stalked flowers or florets
peduncle:	the stalk of a flower
perianth:	the sepals and petals together
petiole:	the stalk of a leaf
phylloclade:	a flattened stem which acts as a leaf = cladode
pinnae:	the parts of a pinnate organ – see next
pinnate:	compound, with the parts arranged on opposite sides of the axis, as in a feather

55

rachide:	rhachis, the axis of a compound leaf or inflorescence
regeneration:	natural regrowth of a plant community after natural or artificial destruction
rhizome:	a spreading, underground stem
ricker:	name given to the pyramidal juvenile form of a kauri tree
serrate:	sharply toothed, teeth pointing forward
stamen:	the pollen-bearing organ of a flower
stigma:.	the part of the female floral structure that receives the pollen
style:	the elongated stalk between stigma and ovary of a flower
terrestrial:	growing on the ground
trifoliate:	having three leaves or leaflets
tomentum:	a dense covering of matted, short hairs
understorey:	layer of trees below the main canopy
viable:	capable of germinating or living

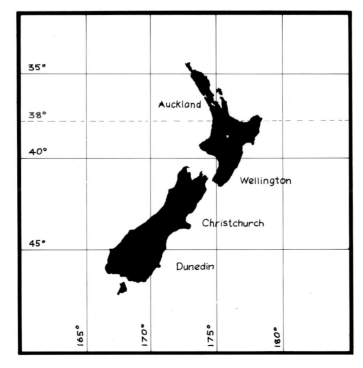

The latitude 38°S. from about Maketu in the east to Kawhia in the west, defines the northerly or southerly distribution limit of many of New Zealand's native trees.

Puriri

Pohutukawa.

Kauri

Tanekaha.

Rimu

Kawaka.